20 MAY 1996
05 MAY 1997

GRAMPIAN REGIONAL
ROSEHEARTY SCHOOL
COUNCIL

Do you know what Grandad did?
He said we could help hang out the washing.
Scruff helped too!

And do you know what else he did?
He broke your china vase…it can’t be mended.
We saved the flowers though!

Mum, Mum, do you know what Grandad did?
He took us to the park and let us get all muddy.
Our shoes are ruined!

And guess what else he did?
He pretended to be a monster in the woods.
Some people saw him!

Mum, do you know what Grandad did?
He let us swing on the front gate.
He had a go too!

Do you know what Grandad did?
He told us about the times *you* were naughty.
A terror you were, said Grandad!

And guess what else he did?

He showed us

how to whistle

with our fingers.

He said you wouldn't mind!

Mum, Mum, do you know what Grandad did?
He taught us a rhyme from when he was a boy.
He says it isn't really rude!

And do you know what else he did?
He bought us bubble-gum...the sort we aren't allowed.
It stuck in my hair!

Do you know what Grandad did?
He had forty winks in the armchair,
And he let us count the snores!

twenty-one
twenty-two
twenty-three
twenty-four

Mum, do you know what Grandad did?
He baked you a surprise cake for tea.

We did the pink icing!

And guess what else he did?
He made us promise not to tell you.

That's what Grandad did!